How to use this guide.

I recommend reading through the guide first to get a feel of th
strategy is there to empower you and help you make adjustm, way, you
currently think and feel.

Please be mindful that sometimes facing and accepting your reality does not always feel positive and you may have tears. This is a good thing! Tears mean you are starting the process of healing. Allow yourself to cry and be kind to yourself. Treat yourself like you would treat your best friend. Once the tears have passed, you will start to feel better slowly.

Remember:

- Some of the examples may not relate to you personally at the moment, simply replace the guide examples with your real life examples.

- You choose the time and place to complete the strategies. You don't have to do it all at once or every day. This guide is meant to support, not overwhelm you.

- You can write in the guide as it is yours or alternatively you may choose to find a nice journal to make your own notes in.

- This guide is private to you - you don't have to share the contents with anyone unless you choose to.

- Repetition is key, so keep reading the guide when you feel like you are having a challenging life event. Flick through the guide whilst asking in your head for the right strategy to help you at the right time. Allow the page to fall open and let the strategy help you resolve the tough time you are facing.

- It may help to share the content with other people you know and trust. Talk together about the strategies and how they apply to each of you.

- You may need extra support on this journey so feel free to check in with a coach, counsellor, therapist, spiritual healer, energy healer, in fact anyone who is qualified in helping another reclaim their power. I do this myself and know how beneficial it is.

So let's together now commit to the journey ahead and reconnect you with the courageous part of you, which has always been there. Remember each day that you commit to your own wellbeing and happiness, you allow others to do the same.

My Declaration To Myself

> I _____

commit to a journey of overcoming my fears and living a life of courageous action where I can learn to love and be loved. I commit to living a life of love, peace, purpose, passion and joy.

SIGNED

_____

DATE

_____

CHAPTER ①

SELF

—

"There are those relationships that open you up to something new and exotic, those that are old and familiar, those that bring up lots of questions, those that bring you somewhere unexpected, those that bring you far from where you started and those that bring you back. But the most exciting, challenging and significant relationship of all is the one you have with yourself. If you can find someone to love the you you love, well that's just fabulous."

Carrie Bradshaw

It is important to have positive intentions about your life. This means thinking positively about how you want your life to be.
Write here why you bought this guide. What was your motivation? Even if you have had the guide bought for you it is still important to take a few minutes to visualise how you want your life to be.

Think about and make notes on

- How is your life different to how you really want it?
- If you had a magic wand, how would you like your life to be?
- Fast forward 6 months - describe how your life will be?

Keep these positive intentions in your mind as you work through this chapter.
On the days when you feel stuck, re-read your notes and remember... you will get there. Courage Queens have determination, patience and self-belief.

Hey Courage Queen!

Well done for being willing to invest your time and energy into completing this guide. Even writing your intentions will help you feel more in control of your life and reduce your stress and tension. When we start to take action, we immediately feel more powerful and less helpless.

Remember these strategies can be used over and over again in all different situations, both at home and work. Other people in your life will also benefit from them too, even children.

A Courage Queen knows the key to any long-term change is consistent effort and focused attention, therefore as a thank you for purchasing this guide we have given you exclusive access to a free PDF download of 'How to be a Courage Queen'.

Please go to www.couragequeen.com/staystrong to access the free download. When you start to feel your Courage Queen power slipping, simply access the PDF and print off the strategy you need to re-balance your power. Even simply reading the strategy will help reframe your thinking and of course this will all be private to you.

Enjoy the journey of becoming stronger and less stressed.

Rachael

I Can Handle... Right Here Right Now

On a regular basis I feel / behave.....(please tick)

Fearful		Courageous	
☐	Fatigued	☐	Energised
☐	Resentful / bitter	☐	Calm
☐	Pessimistic	☐	Optimistic
☐	Fed up / depressed	☐	Inspired / happy
☐	Insecure in self	☐	Secure in own skin
☐	Stressed	☐	Relaxed
☐	Angry constantly	☐	Accepting
☐	Moans and groans	☐	Takes action / motivated
☐	Guilty	☐	Not judgemental
☐	Overwhelmed	☐	Can say No
☐	Self-doubt	☐	Confident / empowered
☐	Fearful of future	☐	Trusting in future
☐	Out of control	☐	OK with not being OK
☐	Uses substances i.e. alcohol / drugs	☐	Use positive ways to relax
☐	Blames others	☐	Take responsibility
☐	Worried / anxious	☐	Trusting of self / others
☐	Escapes / avoids feelings	☐	Embraces feelings
☐	Helpless / stuck	☐	Sets goals & has a vision
☐	Self neglect	☐	Practices self care
☐	Snappy / irritable	☐	Passion for life
☐	Quick to criticise / condemn	☐	Speaks kindly to self

COURAGE QUEEN LEARNING POINT

Ticking the boxes helps you to identify your starting point for creating a more positive way of behaving. A Courage Queen takes responsibility to shift to more courageous ways of thinking, feeling and behaving. She knows she has a right to be happy.

What have you realised about yourself and what would you like to change?

i.e. I would like to be less angry and feel less helpless.

Who or what is causing you to feel this way and what can you do to improve the situation?

i.e. My relationship is not good, I have to seek help or talk to my partner

How will life improve if you use your courage to resolve this situation?

i.e. I would drink less and reduce the arguing - this would help me concentrate at work

"If you constantly build yourself up, nobody can tear you down"

I Can Handle... Solutions

If a miracle happened

Challenge

i.e. Stuck in a rut, Bored!

i.e. I would have a job I love and zest for life

By identifying what is causing you distress, you are able to look for a way forward to improve the situation. It is easy not to face the root cause of our distress, but the problem may continue and may even worsen causing us to become unhappier. A Courage Queen remembers not to let her fear trump her ability to take action.

Now it's your turn......

If a miracle happened

Write here the current
challenges in your life...

Challenge

How could these
challenges be overcome...

*"We regret to inform you that the Universe has
run out of magic wands this week"*

Using the scenario from the previous page, explore what is causing you frustration.

Write here what is causing you frustration...

What choices do I have to resolve this situation?

Because it's MY LIFE!

Pick a choice and ask; what's the worst that could happen?

Pick a choice and ask; what's the best that could happen?

If I do nothing what could happen?

As humans we forget we have many choices available. We often think the worst is going to happen, therefore we don't take action. Taking no action is a choice in itself. As we start to change our behaviour we start to build our confidence as we are learning to handle it! Embracing your courage will help you make the changes which are right for you. A Courage Queen knows taking action is often a solution in itself.

"I am who I am today, because of the choices I made yesterday"

ELEANOR ROOSEVELT

☆ What action(s) do I need to take?

I will do this by _ _ / _ _ / _ _

✒ Declaration

I...give myself permission to take responsibility to take action to improve the frustrating situation. I authorise myself to proceed courageously with the action I have listed above.

Signed ....

Date _ _ / _ _ / _ _

You can do it!
Fear is just an illusion

Rachael

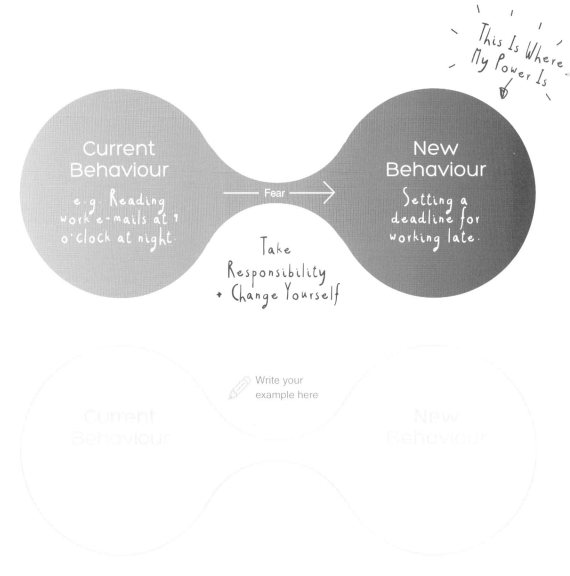

This Is Where My Power Is

Current Behaviour

e.g. Reading work e-mails at 9 o'clock at night.

Fear →

Take Responsibility + Change Yourself

New Behaviour

Setting a deadline for working late.

Write your example here

Current Behaviour

New Behaviour

COURAGE QUEEN · LEARNING POINT

Many of us look to others to change, to make a situation better. However, the only person who has the power to change a situation is ourself. Often when we change our behaviour, this helps the situation to change and we learn to handle new situations. A Courage Queen knows she has the power to change herself.

A Courage Queen may feel helpless and hopeless at times, however behaving in a pro-active way allows her to take her power back.

I will start my new behaviour on

_____ / _____ / _____

If my new behaviour affects others then I need to inform them and will do this by:

_____ / _____ / _____

The positive changes due to my new behaviour will be :

1)

2)

3)

The reason I need to change my current behaviour is :

Remind yourself of this when times get challenging!

"Be the change you
want to see in the world"

Mahatma Gandhi

I Can Handle... The Future

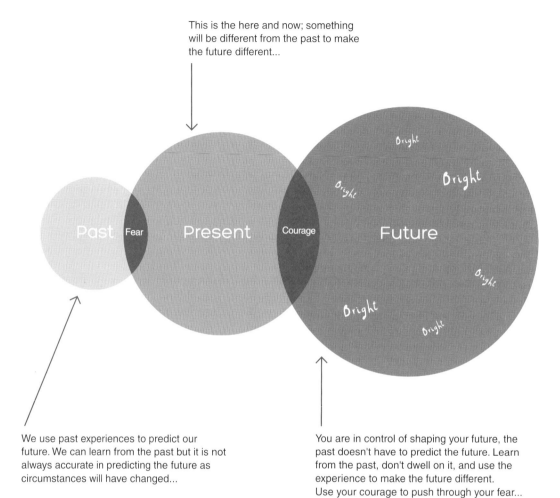

This is the here and now; something will be different from the past to make the future different...

Past | Fear | Present | Courage | Future

Bright *Bright* *Bright* *Bright* *Bright* *Bright*

We use past experiences to predict our future. We can learn from the past but it is not always accurate in predicting the future as circumstances will have changed...

You are in control of shaping your future, the past doesn't have to predict the future. Learn from the past, don't dwell on it, and use the experience to make the future different. Use your courage to push through your fear...

COURAGE QUEEN LEARNING POINT

Many of us use the past to predict the future which is not always a good idea. Whilst the past is a learning experience, the fear of the past being repeated can hold us back. This fear can stop us from taking action and creating a better future. A Courage Queen knows her future can be better than her past.

What do you need to let go of in the past which may be stopping you from creating a better future?

i.e Resenting my ex or changes made at work

How would you like the future to be?

i.e Look for a new job

☆ What are three small steps you can take now?

1)

2)

3)

"The past is a good place to visit but not a great place to stay"

Reasons To Stay The Same

- It's comfortable
- Know colleagues
- Know the job - it's easy
- Don't have to learn new skills
- Don't have to put in any extra effort
- May not be able to do new job
- May dislike new colleagues
- May not like boss
- May not be a job I like
- Don't have to face possible rejection

Change

e.g. Want a new job

Reasons To Change

- Will challenge me
- Will give me confidence
- Know I can handle change
- May make new friends
- Will be good experience
- Will be good on C.V.
- Show me I can take risks
- Can't be as bad as it is now
- Could be a better boss
- Will give me new skills

✎ Reasons To Stay The Same

What would you like to change about life / self?

Reasons To Change

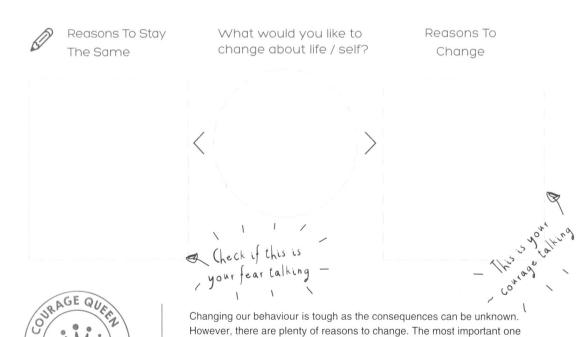

Check if this is your fear talking

This is your courage talking

Changing our behaviour is tough as the consequences can be unknown. However, there are plenty of reasons to change. The most important one being, we show ourselves we can handle the changes, we then become more confident as our fear disappears. A Courage Queen has all the courage she needs to make the changes which are right for her.

COURAGE QUEEN
LEARNING POINT

✎ If I knew I could handle it, what would I choose to do?

After listening to both my fear and courage I choose to :

☐ Stay the same   ☐ Change

✎ Baby steps I can take to make sure my decision works for me:

1)

2)

3)

Resources which can help me handle the unknown:

i.e Positive quotes / coaching / counselling / talking to supportive friend / self-help book

"90% of what we worry about doesn't happen"

Respecting yourself and your needs is important.

Self Respect - Rate your own level of self respect (1 is low, 5 is high)

Know you are a human being, not just a role e.g. parent, employee, boss

Treat yourself to nice things on occasions and celebrate your successes

Speak to yourself kindly with consideration and compassion

Rest and relax when you need to and not feel guilty

Say "No" to others' unrealistic demands without feeling guilty

Give yourself time off to play, chill or do the things you love

Have time on your own to explore your own interests

See the friends and family you want to see

Respect your body by eating and drinking healthily

Understand when you need to let out anger, tears, sadness and frustration

Not take responsibility for everyone else, just yourself

Take responsibility to make your own life better and know you have choices

My Self Respect Score Is:

 /60

Self Respect Score Card	
0-20	Needs Work - Go for it!
21-40	Getting there - well done
41-60	RESPECT!

✎ What are other ways you can show yourself respect.?

i.e. Resting on a day when I think I 'should' clean up!

☆ What action will you take to show yourself more love and respect?

1)

2)

3)

When will you do these steps by?

| / | / |

 Top tip - Learning to meet your own needs is not selfish. Once you can meet your own needs - physical, emotional, mental and spiritual - you are then refuelled to help others you care about.

Respecting yourself is having consideration for your own needs. Once we learn to meet our own needs, we don't need to look to anyone else to meet our needs. Therefore we don't need to control others and are able to love others unconditionally. A Courage Queen demonstrates respecting herself to allow others to respect themselves.

Society

Parents + Childhood

Duty/ Tradition

School & teachers

Relationships

Culture

Life Experiences

Bosses/ Colleagues

What do I think & feel?

What do I believe is unacceptable

How do I act & react

Media

Beliefs formed from age zero. We learn from significant others about

*Roles in life
*Ways to parent
*Work ethic
*Relationships
*Routines/habits
*Religious Views
*Sexuality

Environment

COURAGE QUEEN · LEARNING POINT

Our brain stores beliefs like a filing cabinet. When something happens in our life we check our belief system to see how we should respond. This is automatic behaviour, with little conscious thought, similar to a robot. We can change those beliefs which cause us distress, this will help us to be happier. It is OK to have different beliefs to significant others in our life. A Courage Queen respects her own beliefs.

Complete the boxes with what comes to mind:

I should	I must	I am
i.e. Work harder	i.e. Be nice to everyone	i.e. Stupid

Top Tip - Your answers are 'rules' that you have stored in your filing cabinet. We use these 'rules' to live our life by. However these 'rules' can stop us being happy.

Where did you learn your rules from?
Re-write your rules here into more loving, positive Courage Queen rules

i.e. I will rest more, choose who I am polite to and realise I am intelligent

"I am so much more than what I was brought up to believe"

I Can Handle... Reflecting On My Beliefs

Check out your beliefs - finish the sentences with whatever pops into your mind

1. To say no to others is:

2. To put myself first is:

3. Getting angry is:

4. Crying is:

5. My biggest strength is:

6. The best thing for me to do right now is:

7. Taking time to rest and relax is:

8. I must:

Where do you think you have learned these beliefs from?

Remember you can change your beliefs at any time

Check if your answers are negative and hurtful i.e. crying is wrong. Re-write them into the positive,

- Crying is a normal way to release emotions
- To put myself first is a neccesity sometimes
- Getting angry and expressing it safely is a way to protect myself

"The biggest gift you can give yourself and others is to be self-aware"

The *Louise Hay - Love Yourself, Heal Your Life Workbook* will help you to examine your beliefs.

Rachael

Think of situations which cause you to get angry, withdraw, cry or even moan and groan. These situations have pressed a crumple button, i.e. stroppy email from your boss. Circle or cross the buttons which are at the root cause of your reaction.

Not being liked

Disapproval

Failure

Rejection

Embarrassment & shame

Feeling out of control / helpless

Feeling inadequate

Conflict & confrontation

Disappointing others

Not being respected

Being manipulated

Being seen as selfish

Not being listened to

COURAGE QUEEN LEARNING POINT

Certain situations and people can press our crumple buttons, which is our fear. Once we acknowledge our fear we can learn from it and handle future situations more positively. Our life positively changes when we do not allow our fears to stop us from moving forward with our life. A Courage Queen uses her courage to de-activate her crumple buttons by facing her fears.

Write any other crumple buttons you may have here;

 Guilt

 Self Sabotage

 Being successful

How do you feel when your crumple buttons are pressed?

- [ ] Angry
- [ ] Withdrawn
- [ ] Frightened
- [ ] Derailed
- [ ] Helpless
- [ ] Panicky
- [ ] Want to give up
- [ ] Upset
- [ ] Sick
- [ ] Anxious
- [ ] Fed up
- [ ] Vengeful

Well done, it's OK to feel this way because you are human. The key to change is awareness. Next time your crumple buttons are triggered, remember it is your fear and talk nicely to yourself. The key is to not be scared of your crumple buttons being pressed. A Courage Queen knows she can handle all these inner triggers by not being scared of her crumple buttons.

"No one can make you feel inferior without your consent"

ELEANOR ROOSEVELT

Courage Queen Brain
Uses rational & logical thinking,
loves & respects self. Knows she
can handle it all.

Use positive tools and strategies to
calm fearful brain allowing access to
Courage Queen Brain

Fearful Brain
Worries and anxieties live here
i.e. "I'm fat"

Our thoughts, feelings and
life situations can trigger
our fearful brain

COURAGE QUEEN
LEARNING POINT

Our fearful brain reacts first to situations in life. Once our crumple buttons are pressed we can be overwhelmed with feelings of fear and we therefore panic and may suffer with anxiety and worry. Courage is a form of rational reasoned thinking and it is rooted in love and respect for ourself. A Courage Queen pushes through her fear so her crumple buttons have no power over her.

✏️ I know when I'm acting from my fearful brain / crumple buttons when I....

i.e. overwork, shout and slam the door, sulk

1)

2)

3)

I know when I'm acting from my Courage Queen brain when I

i.e. Respond rather than react, take time out, practice mindfulness.

1)

2)

3)

The best way to shift from my fear to my courage is...

☐ Write down how I feel   ☐ Exercise / Yoga   ☐ Journal out how I feel   ☐ Talk to a friend

☐ Take some time out   ☐ See a Counsellor   ☐ Mindfulness / Meditation   ☐ Get out of my own way

"Face your fear and the fear disappears"

Remember it's human to become overwhelmed by emotion - learn from it and move on

Rachael

I Can Handle... The Fearful Critic Within Me

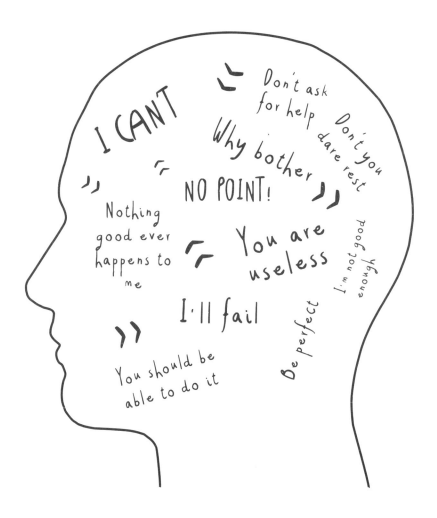

We have fearful thoughts in our head which make us think we can't handle it. These thoughts can be people or experiences from the past which have made us believe we are not enough. A Courage Queen out talks these negative voices using positive self talk.

What is your fearful critic saying to you?

Watch out for your "I should" answers on page **27**

"Once you replace negative thoughts with positive ones, you'll start having positive results"

Well done for being brave and writing them down. Turn over to learn how to manage your thoughts

Rachael

I Can Handle... The Fearful Critic

The situation I need to handle is...

My fearful critic is saying...

The courageous part of you that wants to take responsibility needs to calm this voice by a simple process...

What evidence have I got my critic is speaking the truth?

Your critic often lies

>

What evidence have I got to disprove my critic?

Prove your critic is lying!

What advice would I give a loved one if they told me these critical thoughts?

Once we commit to changes our inner critic may shout louder and then we think we can't handle it. We need to tell ourselves we can handle it which will help us take positive pro-active action, creating a brighter, more positive future. A Courage Queen believes she can overcome any fears she may have and takes action to make positive changes in her life.

☆ What pro-active action can I take which will calm these critical thoughts?

i.e. Send my C.V. off to a recruitment agency

Where have you got the false evidence of your critic from?

i.e. School teacher / family / life experience / media

What positive changes will you see when you take positive action?

i.e. Less arguments at home / job interviews

"To love oneself is the beginning of a lifelong romance"

F alse
E vidence
A ppearing
R eal

I Can Handle... My Emotions

Tick how you handle your emotions...

Emotion	How do I handle it?		Improved way to handle it
Anger	☐	Bottle it up	i.e. Punch pillows
	☐	Shout	
	☐	Drink alcohol	
	☐	Other	
Sadness	☐	Over eat	i.e. Cry
	☐	Bury it	
	☐	Repress it	
	☐	Other	
Frustration	☐	Bang doors	i.e. Talk it over
	☐	Moan & groan	
	☐	Blame	
	☐	Other	
Overwhelmed	☐	Use excuses	i.e. Make a list
	☐	Procrastinate	
	☐	Do nothing	
	☐	Other	
Loss & Grief	☐	Avoid feelings	i.e. See a counsellor
	☐	Denial	
	☐	Distraction	
	☐	Other	

COURAGE QUEEN · LEARNING POINT

Emotions are the way our soul talks to us. By listening and accepting our emotions, they will help us develop as a human and feel psychologically better. We have learnt ways to handle emotions from significant others, however these may not be healthy ways to express our emotions. A Courage Queen respects all her feelings and emotions.

✎ This exercise has shown me...

> i.e. I do not handle anger well

I will learn about my emotions through:

☐ Internet research   ☐ Seeing a counsellor   ☐ Allowing emotions to surface

☐ Finding books about emotions   ☐ Mindfulness   ☐ Journalling

💡 Top Tip - If we suppress or repress our emotions then we can be affected physically. Emotions are energy and need to be expressed safely, even the ones which make us feel sad.

"Feelings are not supposed to be logical- allow them to surface anyway"

WELL DONE! You have taken the most important steps of thinking about yourself and where you are in your life. The greatest ability a human has is to reflect on their life and their behaviour. Take this time to reflect on the most important person in the room... YOU!

What have been the key learning points for you?

What have been your 'lightbulb' moments?

What action have you realised you need to take?

How are you feeling right now?

Remember you have just started your journey. Chapter 2 will give you further ideas on how to embrace your life... DON'T STOP. KEEP GOING!

CHAPTER ②

OTHERS

—

To be nobody but yourself in a world which is doing

it's best, night and day, to make you like everybody else

means to fight the hardest battle which any human being

can fight; and never stop fighting.

E.E Cummings

My Intentions: OTHERS

It is important to have positive intentions about others in your life. This means thinking positively about how you interact with others and the role others play in your life. Visualise your life with significant others in it.

Think about and make notes on

- How do others affect your life?
- How do you want others in your life to be different?
- How will your relationships with others change after you have completed the guide?
- What role do you want others to play in your life?
- How do you act honestly and openly with others in your life?
- How do others act honestly and lovingly with you?

Keep these positive intentions in your mind as you work through this chapter. On the days when you feel stuck, re-read this and remember where you are heading.

Hey Courage Queen!

Well done for being willing to invest your time and energy into completing this guide. Even writing your intentions will help you feel more in control of your life and reduce your stress and tension. When we start to take action, we immediately feel more powerful and less helpless.

Remember these strategies can be used over and over again in all different situations, both at home and work. Other people in your life will also benefit from them too, even children.

A Courage Queen knows the key to any long-term change is consistent effort and focused attention, therefore as a thank you for purchasing this guide we have given you exclusive access to a free PDF download of 'How to be a Courage Queen'.

Please go to www.couragequeen.com/staystrong to access the free download. When you start to feel your Courage Queen power slipping, simply access the PDF and print off the strategy you need to re-balance your power. Even simply reading the strategy will help reframe your thinking and of course this will all be private to you.

Enjoy the journey of becoming stronger and less stressed.

Rachael

Often we want other people to change to make our life better or happier

Who	Angry at...	Complain to...
Wife	Husband	Friends
Husband	Wife	Friends
Colleague	Boss	Colleague
Boss	CEO	Director
Son	Mother	Father
Sister / Brother	Sibling	Parents
Me		

Who do you need to have a conversation with and what about?

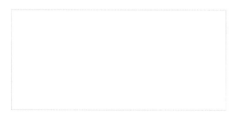

Which crumple buttons are you fearful of being pressed in you and them?

You
i.e. Disapproval

Them
i.e. Conflict

We often complain about another person in our life and wish they would change. However, we complain to the wrong person therefore nothing changes. By having a conversation with the right person, at the right time in the right place we can improve the situation. A Courage Queen has the courage to talk to the person to try and resolve the situation.

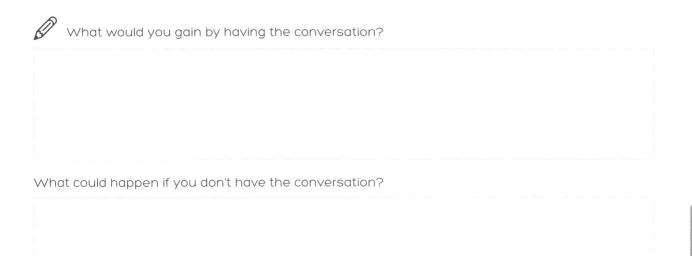

What would you gain by having the conversation?

What could happen if you don't have the conversation?

Top Tip - Even if you have the conversation, nothing may change as the other person may not want to take responsibility. However at least you know you had the courage to have the conversation.

"Have courage to speak your truth with love and humility"

Who causes you worry, stress or frustration?

How may you be taking too much responsibility for them?

How can you allow them to take responsibility for themselves?

How would you feel if you don't take responsibility for them?

Taking too much responsibility for others and not enough for yourself

- Worrying about others
- Getting over-emotional
- Feeling stressed
- Feeling resentful

Not taking enough responsibility for self

- Seeking permission
- Seeking others' approval
- Want to be looked after
- Scared to take action

COURAGE QUEEN
LEARNING POINT

Many of us take far too much responsibility for others as it often makes us feel needed and stops us from looking at our own life. We have to allow others to take responsibility to help them realise they can handle it.

How will you lovingly communicate to the other person you are no longer going to take responsibility for them anymore?

i.e. I know you have the courage to resolve this on your own

How will allowing them to take responsibility for themselves help them?

i.e. It will show them they can take action

What will you gain from allowing them to take responsibility for themselves?

i.e. Not get frustrated when they don't do as I suggest

"We can be compassionate towards others whilst still honouring our own feelings"

Someone's Emotion	Causes Them To	My Response	Better Response
Anger	Slam the door	Shout at them	Walk away to calm down
Crying	Sulk	Try to please them	Let them cry
Anxiety	Worry	Try to reassure	Listen & suggest professional help
Happy	Get giddy	Feel jealous	Help them celebrate
Grief / Loss	Withdraw	Tell them to get over it	Allow them to grieve

Let them have their emotion!

Many of us are emotional caretakers and try to take responsibility for others. We need to allow others to feel and express their own emotions as long as it's not abusive. We also need to be aware of our emotions and how we react. We need to honour all our emotions as it is our internal navigation system to inner peace. A Courage Queen is not afraid of her own emotions or those of others. She shows compassion for herself and others.

List here the people in your life who negatively impact on you :

i.e. Boss, colleague, partner

Write here what you can do to remove yourself or learn not to be affected by their emotions :

i.e. Talk to them about how I feel

 Top Tip - Sadly some people are not willing or may not be able to take responsibility for their life. It is your responsibility to either accept this and keep them in your life or make plans to end the connection.

Others have to learn to manage their emotions - this is not your responsibility. Learn to manage your own reactions

Rachael

What do you use as your medals of martyrdom? (Makes you feel worthy)

i.e. Be the first to volunteer for jobs
i.e. Not take breaks / overwork
i.e. Run about after others
i.e. Not say no to others

What could happen if you take off your medals of martyrdom?

i.e Be less stressed / Meet my needs / Peace

Many of us wear medals of martyrdom as they make us feel worthy. We need to meet our own needs first before we can meet the needs of others. We can burn ourself out trying to meet everyone else's needs but our own. Once we can handle meeting our own needs then we can choose to meet others' needs. A Courage Queen knows it is important to give and receive help.

✏️ In the time I have created by taking off my medals of martyrdom I will:

i.e. Have more time to rest / read more self-help books

1)

2)

3)

I will now prioritise meeting my own needs and my responsibilities in life!

Signed _____

Date _____ / _____ / _____

"Have the courage
to say NO - You are still lovable!"

Having an emotional conversation can be hard as we often don't know how the other person may react. We cannot control how the other person may behave but we can manage our own emotional state.

Before 'THE' Conversation...

1 / How can I take responsibility for this situation arising?

2 / How did I behave or not behave which may have caused the confusion?

3 / What did I say, or not say which may have caused this situation?

4 / Was I honest or did I hide the truth because of fear?

✏️ Who do you need to have a conversation with?

When and where will you do this?

What benefits will having the conversation give you?

What would be the consequences of not having the conversation?

How will you manage any crumple buttons which may get pressed?

"There are 3 versions of this story, mine, yours and then the truth." Gary Barlow & Robbie Williams - 'Shame'

During 'THE' Conversation

1 / Ask the other person what it is like in 'their world' regarding the situation.

Remember to show you have 'heard' them - even if you don't agree.

2 / Explain how you can take responsibility for this situation arising.

3 / Ask them if they think they have any responsibility for this situation arising.

Try to encourage them to take responsibility as this will empower them.

4 / Together, what is your plan of action to resolve the situation, remembering to learn from it?

How will you ensure you stay calm and rational during the conversation?

What positive outcome do you visualise for you both?

Top Tip - Remember it is OK to take time out if the conversation gets heated. Your crumple buttons may have been triggered. Letting the emotion 'drain away' will help your rational thoughts kick in. Just remember to come back to the conversation later.

"You have two ears and one mouth for a reason"

After 'THE' conversation...

1 / Congratulate

Congratulate yourselves that the situation has been resolved and you have had 'THE' conversation. This is how trust and intimacy builds in relationships

2 / Reflect

Reflect on what you have learned about :

Self

Situation

Others

Having a difficult conversation can be emotionally charged as we are often showing our true feelings. We need to prepare and have the conversation in a positive manner. To show vulnerability is to show courage. Courage Queens know they can be vulnerable - this is an act of power.

How has this conversation helped you for the future?

i.e. Made me realise I can talk things over

Who else do you need to have an honest conversation with?

Write the subject here.

When and where will you have this next conversation?

i.e. Next Friday in the house.

"We are all pebbles from the same shore"

I Can Handle... Setting Boundaries

What are boundaries?

· **What you will/will not accept**
· **What you want/don't want**
· **What is good for you**
· **What will stop you feeling frustrated**

Examples of boundaries :

· **Child going to bed at 8.00pm**
· **Parent not just 'popping in'**
· **Taking time off**
· **Not working past 7.00pm**

Which boundary can you implement to improve your wellbeing?

How might people react?

Which crumple buttons may get pressed in them and me?

Them

Me

Saying 'No' is essential to our well-being. Many of us are manipulated by others because we don't have secure boundaries and we then spend time feeling frustrated, resentful and guilty. By knowing your boundaries and communicating them to others will help you and them to feel happier.

☆ What action do you need to take now? (including communicating the boundaries)

i.e. Tell her I will not be taking her to work anymore if she is late.

How will you manage yourself and others who do not respect your boundaries?

i.e. I will repeat the boundary once but then leave at specified time.

How often will you review your boundaries?

i.e. Weekly at first, then monthly.

"Not setting boundaries is like leaving all your windows open and your key in the door. People will walk right in and take what they want"

RACHAEL ALEXANDER

You may need to put a reminder up about your boundaries to help change your behaviour

Rachael

When people press our crumple buttons we often react from our fearful brain rather than responding from our Courage Queen brain.

Reacting ⟶ Responding

i.e. A colleague sends you an email which appears defensive and critical of you.

1 / Honour the emotion

What is it telling you? Which crumple button has been pressed? Disapproval/criticism? Deactivate your crumple button by talking kindly to yourself.

>

2 / Respond

If you are confused, clarify the message - What is the other person really saying?

"I'm confused - what are you saying?"

3 / Take responsibility

What do you need to take responsibility for - do you need to apologise, own anything or is it 'their stuff'? Leave it with them if it's 'their stuff'.

>

4 / Expression

Express your own feelings, what do you really want to say?

"I'm wondering if I am being sensitive, however, I sense you are angry with me, can we talk about it?"

Many of us react to situations out of fear and we make assumptions with often no evidence of what is the truth. We need to take responsibility to make the situation work for all parties so that we can all live together harmoniously. A Courage Queen investigates her beliefs to see why she reacted in the way she did.

What are you overreacting about?

i.e. Argument with my partner

How have you reacted rather than responded?

i.e. Stormed out of house and sulked for two days.

How could you have responded rather than reacted?

i.e. Take time out then express how I feel calmly

What have you learnt about yourself and the situation from overreacting?

i.e. The situation pressed my 'not being respected' crumple button.

② OTHERS

"We spend too much time in our lives over thinking and overreacting"

Saying sorry is a true act of courage as long as it's followed with, "and this is how I won't let it happen again"

Rachael

Chapter Review

Another part of the journey completed. You are doing great!
If you can get into the habit of reflecting on your thinking and behaviour you will continue to become stronger and more confident. This is getting the most out of this experience called LIFE. Take time to reflect on…

What has been the most important learning point for you?

What have been your 'lightbulb' moments?

What needs to change in your life?

I trust you will now be starting to feel stronger. A Courage Queen will need to handle all situations which occur in her life. Chapter 3 will show you more ways to handle whatever happens.

LIFE

—

"To be a star you must shine your own light, follow your own path and not worry about the darkness, for that is where the stars shine the brightest..."

Author Unknown

My Intentions: LIFE

It is important to have positive intentions about your life. This means thinking positively about how you want your life to be.

Think about and make notes on

- How is your life different to how you really want it?
- If you had a magic wand, how would you like your life to be?
- Fast forward 6 months - describe how would you like your life to be?
- What needs to change in your life?

Keep these positive intentions in your mind as you work through this chapter. On the days when you feel stuck, re-read your notes and remember where you are heading.

Hey Courage Queen!

Well done for being willing to invest your time and energy into completing this guide. Even writing your intentions will help you feel more in control of your life and reduce your stress and tension. When we start to take action, we immediately feel more powerful and less helpless.

Remember these strategies can be used over and over again in all different situations, both at home and work. Other people in your life will also benefit from them too, even children.

A Courage Queen knows the key to any long-term change is consistent effort and focused attention, therefore as a thank you for purchasing this guide we have given you exclusive access to a free PDF download of 'How to be a Courage Queen'.

Please go to www.couragequeen.com/staystrong to access the free download. When you start to feel your Courage Queen power slipping, simply access the PDF and print off the strategy you need to re-balance your power. Even simply reading the strategy will help reframe your thinking and of course this will all be private to you.

Enjoy the journey of becoming stronger and less stressed.

Rachael

I Can Handle... A Meaningful Life

What makes my life worthwhile?

Internal Attributes

- Give unconditionally
- Receive unconditionally
- Humour
- Caring to others
- Positive attitude
- Courage
- Humility
- Calm in rough seas
- Healthy relationships
- Tenacity
- Kindness
- Respect

 Add Your Ideas

> i.e. Nature, sunrise, sunset, read a book

The Universe can never take these away as they are a state of mind, attitude and a way of being. If we have the above we can have true confidence as our inner self knows it really is good enough and can handle it. A Courage Queen is strong internally.

External Resources

- Millionaire mentality
- Gadgets
- Job titles
- House size
- Car type
- Accessories
- Jewellery
- Celebritydom
- Brands
- Name dropping
- Status
- Overspending

Add Your Ideas

> i.e. House in 'good' area, money

The Universe can take these away at any moment so we never feel safe or secure. These things do not give true self confidence as they are not coming from within. Therefore our inner self still thinks it is not good enough and can't handle it. Things cannot love us back!

Work on the inside stuff and it allows you to enjoy the outside stuff!

Working on your internal attributes allows us to enjoy the external resources more. It is important not to get our self-worth and identity from external resources. These do not fill the void inside, only love from oneself can do this. A Courage Queen knows her self-worth comes from building her internal attributes.

Where have I got the idea from that external resources are more important than strong internal attributes?

i.e. Media / advertisements / conditioning from culture

How can I build my internal attributes more?

i.e. Learn to be more positive, stop overspending

Top Tip - Following a more spiritual way of living can help to build a strong sense of self. Spirituality is not necessarily the same as being religious.

"Your true wealth lies in your relationships not your possessions"

I Can Handle... A Positive Environment

	Positive Influences	Negative Influences
People	Best mate	Boss
TV/ Film	Inspirational Stories	Soap Operas
Music	Inspirational Lyrics	Depressing Lyrics
Ways to spend time	Reading Self-Help Books	Complaining to Friends
Internet	Inspirational Websites	Uninspiring Facebook posts

Our environment is really important to us. Our surroundings can affect our emotions. Choose your environment wisely. It may mean letting go of old habits and people. Start to hang out with people who want to be positive. Watching the news before you go to sleep can cause you to feel helpless and out of control. A Courage Queen is responsible for creating a positive environment around her.

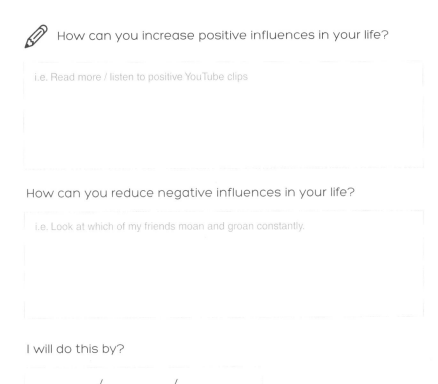

How can you increase positive influences in your life?

i.e. Read more / listen to positive YouTube clips

How can you reduce negative influences in your life?

i.e. Look at which of my friends moan and groan constantly.

I will do this by?

/   /

To see positivity wherever you go, you need to stimulate your brain with:

Music / Make positive play lists.

Lyrics / Print lyrics out to keep positive and collect them in journals.

Journal / Write down how you feel to get your emotions out.

Quotes / Stick them around the house or in journals.

Affirmations / Google affirmations - sign up to positive newsletters and websites.

"If you hang around with chickens you are going to cluck, if you hang around with eagles you are going to fly"

3 LIFE

Think about your average week. What activities would go in each box?

Work
i.e. 9-5, food shopping, housework

Play
i.e. Being creative, meeting friends, dancing

Rest
i.e. Relaxing, watching films, yoga, have Reiki

Purpose & Passion
i.e. How can your future be filled with passion and purpose?

Too much energy in any one section and the balance will tip

COURAGE QUEEN LEARNING POINT

We are vessels of energy, therefore it is important to have a balance of work, rest and play. It is also important to think about planning for your future. Where would you like to be in two, five, or ten years time? A Courage Queen knows it's important to work, rest and play. She has a vision for the future which fills her with purpose and passion.

☆ What are four action steps you can take to help balance your life?

1) _____ / ____ / ____

2) _____ / ____ / ____

3) _____ / ____ / ____

4) _____ / ____ / ____

💡 Top Tip - Sometimes we may have received messages that it is weak to rest. This is untrue, rest is important to our well being.

"Everything you do determines the sort of world our children will live in"

I Can Handle... My Life Experiences

Taking responsibility means learning from our life experiences. Think about a situation which is frustrating you and identify what you can learn from it.

I Can't Handle Taking Responsibility

Reality

i.e. Argument with partner

- Moans & groans
- Blames something
- Blames someone else
- Gives up
- Critical to self/others
- Shouts at others
- Sulks
- Abuses self e.g. drink/drugs

I Can Handle Taking Responsibility

- Expresses the emotion
- Why did it happen?
- Lessons learned?
- Identifies who is responsible
- Do differently next time?
- Give self compassion
- Let go and move on
- Apologies without 'but'...

The more you can learn from tough situations, the stronger internally you are becoming.

Often we don't like to face reality because it can be emotionally painful. We choose not to take responsibility to improve the situation, however, this keeps us stuck. It is only by taking responsibility that we can show ourselves we can handle reality. A Courage Queen learns from every experience which makes her stronger and able to handle life with strength, grace and dignity.

Who or what is frustrating you?

> i.e. Ex-partner, workplace

How can you take responsibility to learn from this situation?

> i.e.Reflect on why I got angry. What crumple button got pressed?

How can you reframe this perceived negative experience into a positive one?

> i.e.It taught me that next time I need to say 'No" more quickly

"The more you take responsibility for your past and present the more you are able to create the future you seek"

(3)

LIFE

I Can Handle... Moving On

Forgiveness & compassion for self and others. Unconditional love

Action
Take steps to improve the situation and situation starts to change.

10

9 **Trust & Accept Help**
Trust in self and accept help from others, have faith in the Universe to help.

Take Responsibility
I can do something to change this situation, nobody else can.

8

7 **Courage**
Believe I have a right to happiness and I can change things.

Acceptance
I have to do something and change. Allow emotions to be discharged.

6

Can keep getting stuck and going round and round at this point and start to blame again, or you can move up to acceptance...

Self Sabotage
Anger, upset, anxious, use of food/alcohol/drugs.

5

4 **Frustration**
I can't change this situation – it's them not me that have created this.

Confusion
Why am I feeling like this, it's not right?

3

2 **Realisation**
Something has to change - I can't go on like this or my mental health will start to suffer.

Denial / Blame
Annoyance, moaning/groaning, emotional turmoil.

1

Fear

A Courage Queen knows she can move on from challenging situations. Staying stuck can affect her mental, physical and emotional well being. The more she pushes through her fear, the more she will have unconditional love for herself and others.

What do you need to move on from?

i.e. Self sabotage stage: Using food to comfort me.

How can you take baby steps to move to the next stage of change?

i.e. Acceptance stage: Acknowledge how I feel and express my emotions safely

 Top Tip - With any change comes 'loss'. Moving through grief and loss is an important life stage. Explore the life cycle of loss by Elisabeth Kübler-Ross to help your transition through this chapter in your life.

"Sometimes you have to be flat on your back to be able to see the stars"

I Can Handle... Expectations

Ultra High / Perfectionist Expectations of Self and Others

No one can achieve all expectations, including yourself (can cause stress and burn out)

i.e. Cooking a complicated meal every night

Reasonable Expectations of Self and Others

This is having love and respect for yourself

i.e. Having an easy but nutritious meal after a long day at work.

Low Expectations of Self and Others

i.e. Having take-aways every night.

Not a good place (gutter expectations)

We have to be aware of the expectations that others place on us and that we place on ourself. Some expectations are unrealistic and cause us stress. Having reasonable expectations of ourself leads us to a positive place. Having expectations about others can sometimes lead to disappointment. A Courage Queen monitors expectations of herself and others.

List three reasonable expectations you will have of yourself moving forwards :

1)

2)

3)

Often we speak in 'shoulds'. These are ways in which we think we should think and behave. We have picked these ideas up from other people in our life. 'Shoulds' often lead to perfectionist expectations. See what 'shoulds' you have around your current challenges in life.

I should...
be working harder
be a better mum

 Top Tip - Change your 'shoulds' to 'coulds' and you are in a position of choice which reduces guilt.

"The perfect is the enemy of the good" Voltaire

I Can Handle... Switching Off

leave your work mindset for the day >

What am I over thinking?

> i.e. Work, relationships, future

What helps me relax?

> i.e. Walking, meditation, laughing at T.V.

Our brain can drive us insane with its constant over thinking and analysing. We need to find ways to relax our brain. Even just imagining walking out of the room of over thinking and into a room of relaxation can help. A Courage Queen knows she has to relax her mind and body. This is an act of self love.

I will use the following ways to relax:

i.e. Mindfulness app, bath with candles

Top Tip - Commit to a relaxation method and routine. Remember you are of no use to others if you burn yourself out.

"Relax after you have worked hard. Relaxing is just as important as work".

You can't give to others if your cup is empty

Rachael

LIFE

Congratulations
You have learnt how to be a Courage Queen!

What have been the key learning points in the last chapter?

What have you realised about yourself?

What could you change to handle it better?

What are your next steps for continuing to take responsibility to improve your life?

Who can help you?

WELL DONE! I hope you continue to make choices which are right for you
Remember... YOU CAN HANDLE IT!

CONGRATULATIONS

I hereby crown

insert your name here

a Courage Queen. Your strength, courage and grace will take you to many positive places.

Enjoy the journey.

Rachael Alexander

Remember - When you step into your Courage Queen shoes and demonstrate self-respect, you are giving other women permission to do the same. Let's help all women to straighten their crown and move forward with their life.

Rach
X

A personal message from Rachael Alexander

I am so proud that you have taken responsibility and taught yourself how to think, feel and behave more positively. The key to success in anything is consistency so keep this guide somewhere handy where you can keep reminding yourself of the ideas. Remember when you have a 'wobble' and a life experience steals your power, this guide will remind you how to get your power back! Even the most successful people know they can reach out and ask others for help. I myself see professionals who help me stay strong and feel blessed they are in my life.

We recommend you reach out to:

- Counsellors/Coaches/Therapists
- Local NHS services including mental health services
- Hypnotherapists/Kinesiologists/EFT Therapists
- Spiritual Healing such as Reiki, Shamanism and Crystal Healing
- Spiritual Readers including Astrologers/Tarot/Clairvoyants
- Charities such as Relate and Mind

Make sure you seek recommendations and talk to them first to make sure you get a good vibe from them. We also strongly recommend reading self-help books, watching YouTube videos and use positive social media to help you on your journey.

Sign up to my Courage Queen Club on my website **www.couragequeen.com**. You will be the first to receive blogs and articles which talk about ways in which I keep myself strong and continually use courage to trump my fear. Finally, the most important advice of all, remember to sit quietly and ask the Universe to send you what you need to help you on this exciting adventure called life.

From my courageous heart to yours -

Rachael Alexander

 @Couragequeen

 @TheCourageQueen

 thecouragequeen

PS Please remember to download your free pdf version of the book at www.couragequeen.com/staystrong
PPS Calling all therapists - If you resonate with this material and would like to be part of delivering the Courage Queen message, please contact us at: www.CourageQueen.com